The Publishers wish to thank the following for their assistance:-

Linda Meredith School of Make-up
60, Church Road, Leyton, London, E10

Cosmetics:-
Yves St Laurent
Florrie Roberts
Fashion Fair Cosmetics
Redken
Jerome Alexander
Stagelight
Charles of The Ritz
Clinique
Elizabeth Arden

Accessories, clothes etc:-
Alexandre de Paris (make-up brushes)
Liberated Lady
Quasimodo Ltd
Pineapple Dance Studio
Hat Shop, Covent Garden

**Photography by Peter Barry**
**Designed by Philip Clucas**
**Produced by Ted Smart and David Gibbon**

This edition published 1985 by Book Club Associates
by arrangement with Colour Library Books.
CLB 1327
© 1985 Illustrations and text: Colour Library Books Ltd.,
    Guildford, Surrey, England.
Display and text filmsetting by Acesetters Ltd., Richmond, Surrey, England.
Produced by AGSA in Barcelona, Spain.
Colour separations by Llovet, S.A., Barcelona, Spain.
Printed and bound in Barcelona, Spain by Rieusset and Eurobinder.
All rights reserved.
ISBN 0 86283 339 6

# 10 Easy Steps to Perfect Make-Up

Text and Make-Up by Linda Meredith

**GUILD PUBLISHING**
**LONDON**

# Contents

# Introduction

Many different looks are achieved through skilled use of make-up and clever, informed choice of the many cosmetics and textures available to us today.

The aim of this book is to take the 'science' out of the 'art' of make-up, because it is an area that has become unnecessarily complicated. The book teaches you the valuable basic make-up skills in a logical, step-by-step way and explains the reasons behind the methods. The techniques, colour application and choice of cosmetics described within are straightforward, professional and effective. There is simply no need to complicate them. You will find that some of the techniques go against what is generally accepted in the make-up

world. This is because these new ideas have been tried and tested and found to be simpler and, in many cases, more effective than the established ones.

Once you have mastered the basic skills of make-up you can have the fun of experimenting with new ideas, or simply perfecting the style which you feel is right for you. In either case this book provides the solid groundwork necessary, and there are plenty of photographs and tips throughout to spark the imagination.

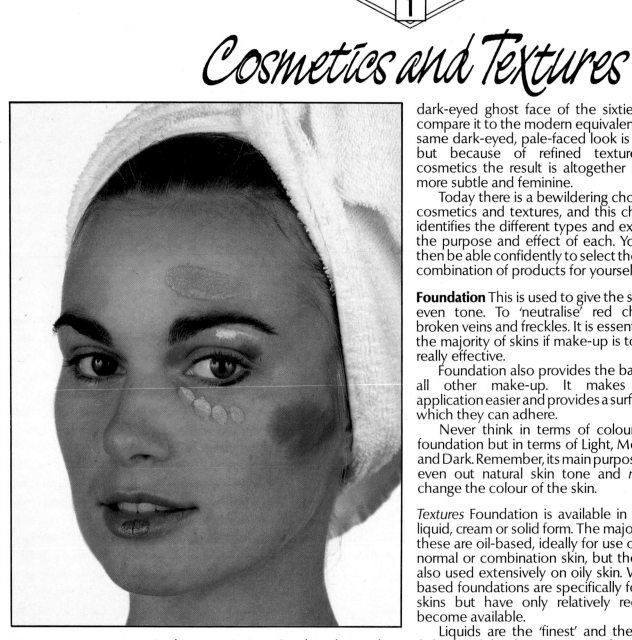

# CHAPTER 1

# Cosmetics and Textures

dark-eyed ghost face of the sixties and compare it to the modern equivalent. The same dark-eyed, pale-faced look is there, but because of refined textures of cosmetics the result is altogether softer, more subtle and feminine.

Today there is a bewildering choice of cosmetics and textures, and this chapter identifies the different types and explains the purpose and effect of each. You will then be able confidently to select the right combination of products for yourself.

**Foundation** This is used to give the skin an even tone. To 'neutralise' red cheeks, broken veins and freckles. It is essential on the majority of skins if make-up is to look really effective.

Foundation also provides the base for all other make-up. It makes their application easier and provides a surface to which they can adhere.

Never think in terms of colour with foundation but in terms of Light, Medium and Dark. Remember, its main purpose is to even out natural skin tone and *not* to change the colour of the skin.

*Textures* Foundation is available in either liquid, cream or solid form. The majority of these are oil-based, ideally for use on dry, normal or combination skin, but they are also used extensively on oily skin. Water-based foundations are specifically for oily skins but have only relatively recently become available.

Liquids are the 'finest' and therefore 'lightest' of the three textures. They allow the normal skin tone to glow through and so give a smooth but natural look. Concealers can be used underneath to hide blemishes, dark circles under the eyes, etc. Liquid foundation should always be used for a day make-up unless your skin has a problem with widespread blemishes which dictate the need for extra cover. In which case...

Creams are 'heavier' than liquids and so

(Above) showing some of the many different cosmetics available. Shown are lipstick, foundation, blusher, contour, highlighter (on brow) and eye shadows.

Each cosmetic item (i.e. foundation, face powder, blusher, eye shadow, etc.) offers a choice of textures which could include liquid, cream, block, gel, powder, cream powder and so on. These textures dictate the end result of a make-up. And to highlight the dramatic effect that changes in the formulations of textures have on the finished 'product' we can draw a parallel between two identical make-ups. Look at the photograph of the heavily pan-sticked,

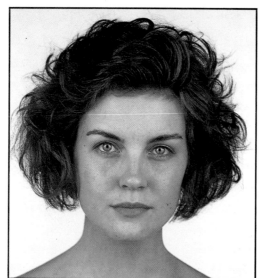

Even at a distance quite mild imperfections ruin the even skin tone effect essential to a perfect make-up look (right)

for 'normal' make-up as it is excessively heavy and obvious; it is therefore not mentioned again in this book.

*'Tools' you need.* Dot liquid and cream foundation with an eye shadow shading brush and blend with a sponge.

**Tinted Gels and Tinted Moisturisers** These are not classed as foundations as they do not give any coverage. However, they are acceptable as a base for make-up if used on a fairly even skin tone. They can be successful in giving skin a healthy glow or a tanned look. Loose or Block Powder can be applied on top.

*'Tools' you need.* Apply with fingers.

**Face Powder** The main purpose of face powder is to 'set' the foundation which would otherwise, within two to three

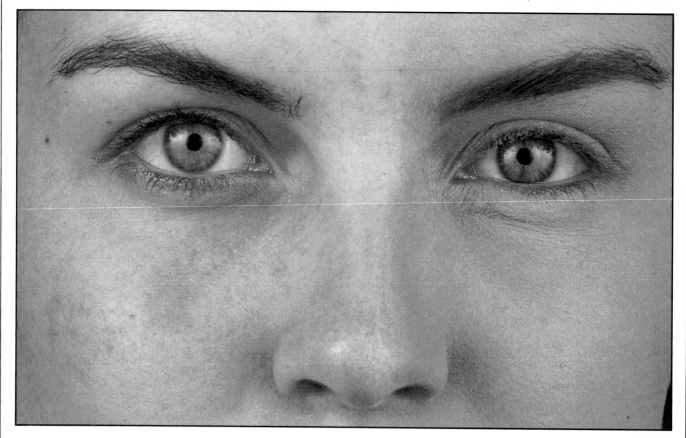

Clever use of foundation, powder (and concealer if necessary) disguises our faults and evens out skin tone for the colour cosmetics to follow.

give extra cover to skin with very obvious problems. No concealer is needed. But because the creams are heavier they are also more noticeable and so you should look to the more subtle forms of concealing before deciding that you need a cream foundation.

Solids create a mask or marble-like effect. Popular in the sixties, today they are only used for dramatic effect in photography, for theatrical purposes and fashion shows. A solid must never be used

hours, slide off the skin. It also gives staying power to lipstick, and prevents cream blusher and cream eye shadow from creasing. Face powder is the essential finishing touch to all good make-up.

Except for special effect, face powder is not used to add colour to the face. Those powders that are coloured today contain a tint which makes them light in texture, unlike the very heavy powders of yesteryear which contained a pigment.

Translucent powder is the most

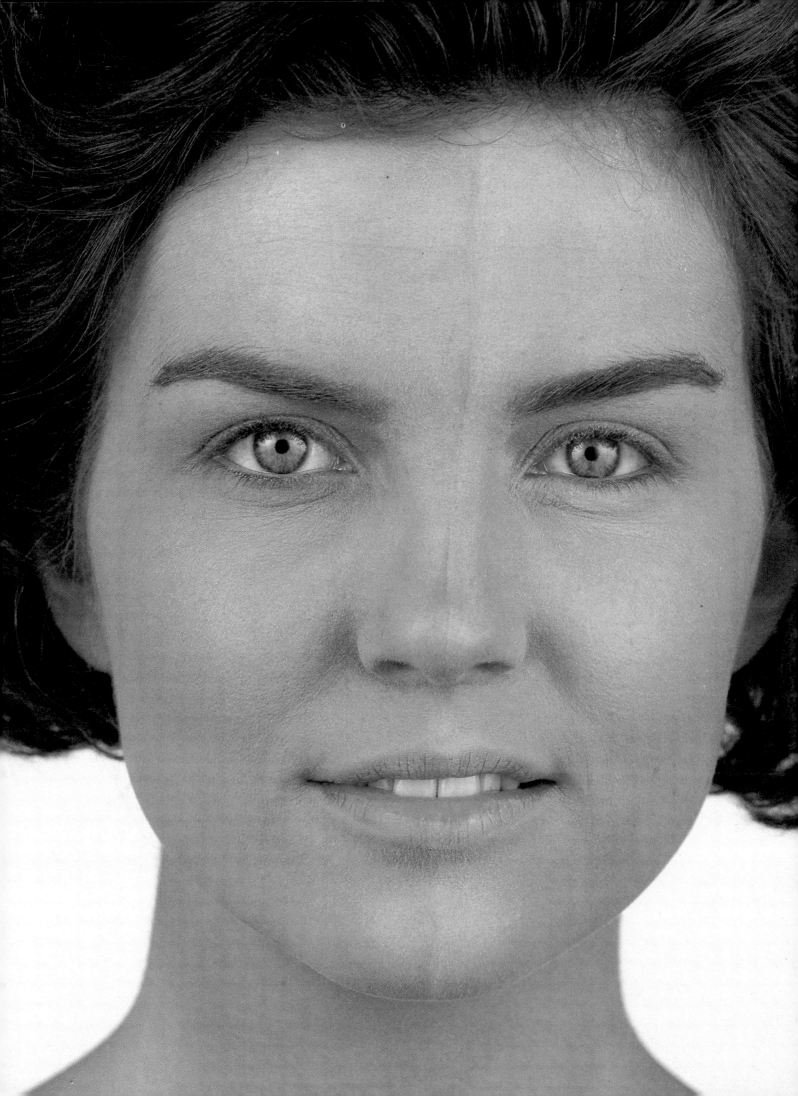

(Below) liquid foundation and block powder give a light, translucent look on older skin. (Opposite) cream foundation and loose powder cover widespread blemishes.

commonly used today. It is usually colourless, although some do carry a hint of colour. In either case 'translucent' means that it allows the natural skin tone to glow through.

Transparent powder is always completely colourless.

*Textures* Face powder is available in two forms: Loose, which comes in a 'tub' container, and block, which is a compressed form of loose powder and is presented as a solid block.

Block powder is the finest of the two textures and is used to 'set' liquid foundation. Cream foundation is too heavy to be set with block powder.

Many people still think that block is heavier than loose powder. A very simple experiment proves the opposite. Fill a face powder brush with block powder and flick the bristles with your fingers. You will see only a very, very fine dust. If you were to do the same with loose powder its heavier particles would be very obvious! But the ultimate test is in application. Any amount

(Right) a simple flick test proving that block powder is much finer than loose powder. (Opposite page) a perfect finished make-up using the finest cosmetic textures.

Loose powder is also important if you have very oily skin as it can be used on top of liquid foundation to help absorb excess oil. The absorption is helped both by the consistency of the powder and by the method of application, (i.e. you press the powder onto the skin with cotton wool or powder puff).

*'Tools' you need.* Powder puff and/or cotton wool balls.

**Concealers** These are necessary to 'blot' out dark shadows under eyes, broken veins, high cheek colour and simple spots and blemishes. They are generally applied before foundation (but remember that cream foundation does its own concealing).

*Textures* Concealers come in sticks or as thick cream with their own applicators. They are oil-based or water-based; the

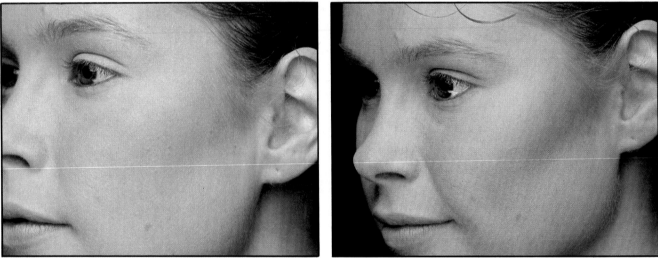

(Above) indicating correct position for blusher and (above right) finished blusher application, showing it to be one of the most flattering of the colour cosmetics. It accentuates the cheekbones and adds colour and warmth to the skin.

of block powder can be applied to a face without it being apparent. Too much loose powder will very quickly look heavy and unnatural.

So, the combination of block powder and liquid foundation creates the smoothest, most natural look and should be used whenever possible in daytime make-up.

*'Tools' you need.* Face powder brush for dusting powder over face. Do not use the flat powder puff which is usually supplied with blocks as this makes application too heavy.

Loose powder is heavier in texture than block and can be more obvious on the skin. But it is essential to use loose powder over cream foundation. This is because the thicker consistency of the cream texture needs the extra setting power of loose powder.

latter has more staying power.

*'Tools' you need.* Small brush to apply concealer and dry latex sponge to blend in.

**Blusher** This is the first of the colour cosmetics that you apply to your face and one of the most flattering. Its main purpose is to accentuate the cheek bones and to add colour and warmth to the skin. Cleverly and selectively dotted around the face it gives the impression of a soft healthy glow, an effect which benefits all ages.

Blushers come in a great variety of colours and shades. In day make-up they cancel out the need for contours and highlighters.

*Textures* There is a wide choice of tetures: Solid Cream; Liquid Cream; Gels; Sticks and Pencils and Powder. The most popular and easy to apply is powder blusher. This is

mainly because of the form of application. The blusher brush is specially shaped to help you apply the colour to the correct cheekbone area; it helps you avoid too heavy an application as it gives only a fine dusting; and it is the perfect 'tool' with which to blend the blusher down the cheekbone. All other blushers are applied direct from their applicators or by fingertip. These methods give less control over shape, are likely to deliver too high a density of colour, and make blending less efficient.

*'Tools' you need.* Blusher brush.

*'Tools' you need.* A short, stiff nylon brush (eyebrow brush) with which to apply powder or to soften hard pencil lines.

**Eye Shadows** These give colour, definition and shape to the eyes.

*Textures* Cream powder, as it's name suggests, is a combination of cream and powder. It is the most commonly used form of eye shadow. Presented as a powder it

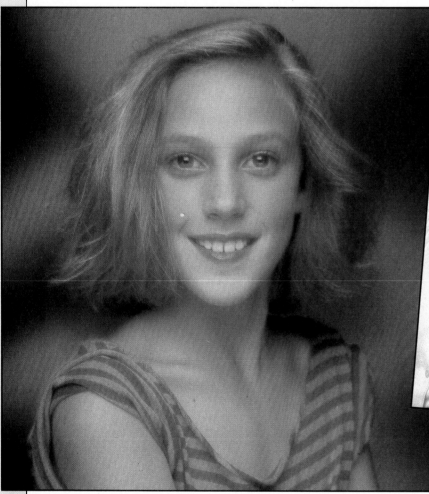

No matter what your age, skin type, or skin problem, the range of cosmetics and their various textures make it possible for us all to present a more positive and 'colourful' face to the world.

**Eyebrow Colour** To add colour to the eyebrows.

*Textures* Eyebrow colours are either in the form of a pencil or a powder. Eye shadow colours can also be used on the eyebrows, (although eyeliner pencils are softer than eyebrow pencils and so do not apply colour as effectively). It is easier to achieve a soft natural effect with powder but hard pencil lines can be softened quite easily, and this technique is explained elsewhere in this book.

has a creamy texture and gives the staying power of cream with the soft look of powder.

*'Tools' you need.* An angled eye shadow brush.

Loose powder has become increasingly popular and, unlike loose face powder, it blends very finely onto the skin, (and is, in fact, the finest textured of all eye shadows). It is only available in frosted colours, some of which are very vibrant and therefore effective for a special evening occasion. The neutral colours are ideal as a base for day make-up if finely blended over the entire eye area.

*'Tools' you need.* A sponge-tipped applicator.

(Opposite page) the textures of today's cosmetics allow much easier and more comfortable application of make-up. This makes the morning routine a much less harassed affair!

(Right) a face beautifully finished with foundation and face powder. Always use the finest textures when possible, for the smoothest and most natural look. This means liquid foundation (only cream if a skin problem is severe or widespread), and 'set' with translucent block powder (but loose powder has to be used to 'set' the heavier cream foundation).

(Right) eyeshadow and eyeliner pencils have a cream powder texture and their staying power is therefore good. To keep a good point for eyelining, sharpen as an ordinary pencil and pop in the fridge for 15-20 minutes. But allow to return to normal before applying to eyes.

Block powder, unlike its face powder counterpart, tends to have a concentrated look on the skin. It can also appear dry and flaky on the eyelid and has no real staying power.

*'Tools' you need.* An angled eye shadow brush.

Cream shadow lasts all day but easily creases and must always be 'set' with face powder.

*'Tools' you need.* A sponge-tipped applicator.

Eye shadow wands come with their own sponge tipped applicator and are available in cream or powder form.

Eye liner pencils look like ordinary pencils and come in many different colours. Its texture is that of a cream powder

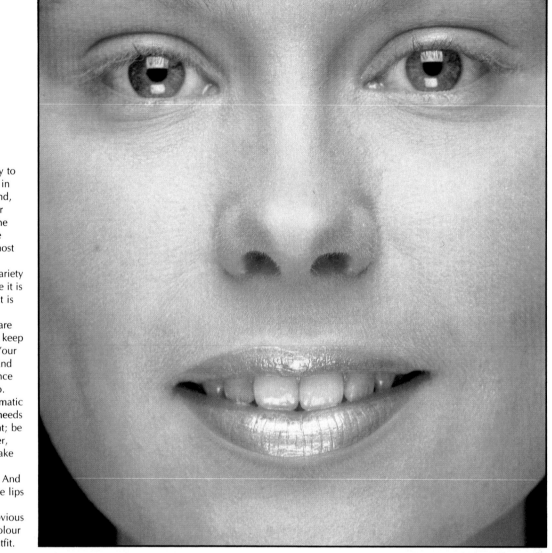

Lipstick, lipstick, everywhere... and plenty to spare! The colour range in lipsticks is marvellous and, combined with the softer textures and choice of the glossy glamour look, the lipstick is possibly the most potent of all cosmetics. Perhaps because of the variety of lipsticks now available it is an area of cosmetics that is frequently misused and abused. The guidelines are quite simple and should keep you on the right track. Your lipstick colour, texture and application should balance the rest of your make-up. Dramatic eyes need dramatic lips; subtle eyeshading needs harmonious lip treatment; be it in colour shade (lighter, darker) or technique, make sure that lips and eyes balance each other out. And don't forget to harmonise lips with clothes. A badly matched lipstick is as obvious as wearing the wrong colour bag or shoes with an outfit.

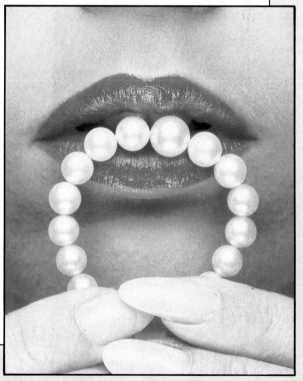

shadow and therefore it has good staying power. Keep a good point on your eyeliner pencil by using an ordinary pencil sharpener, then pop the pencil in the refrigerator for 15 to 20 minutes to harden it. But allow it to return to normal before applying to your lids.

(Above) one of the most flattering of all cosmetics. Those available today include water-proof, those which thicken and even some which lengthen lashes. (Opposite page) choose a coloured mascara to emphasise a colour theme further, or simply as extra interest in your make-up.

**Lipstick** This is used to balance the made-up face and to emphasise the mouth. In other words, if the eyes are exaggerated the lips should be also (with colour and outline); if the eyes are soft and natural, lipstick colour should follow suit, with subtle outline definition if necessary.

*Textures* The original lipstick, by Yardley, was called 'Stayfast' and quite literally stayed on for days! Today, lipsticks have a much softer texture and the majority need to be dusted with face powder to help them last a reasonable time. Soft, glossy lipsticks should not be blotted as this removes all colour from the lips. Lip pencils can be used directly on the lips but it is difficult to achieve a clean outline this way. It is much better to take the lipstick off the pencil with a lip brush. Lip gloss is a flattering cosmetic and the finishing touch

over lipstick to give a soft, glamorous look. It can be tinted or clear, and can be used on its own to complement very softly made-up eyes.

*'Tools' you need.* A lip brush and tissues.

**Highlighter** This is generally used for dramatic effects, although subtle use of highlighter gives a flattering 'lift' to a face. Areas on which highlighter is used are the browbone, top of the cheekbone and the centre of the top lip. The colours are usually white or light cream.

*Textures* Highlighters are available as either cream or powder. Preference should be given to the one you find easiest to work with.

*'Tools' you need.* Contour brush.

**Shaders and Contours** Shaders are always brown, and are used around the face to give a slimming effect where needed, or to make areas recede.

Contours are generally brown but can be substituted with dark blusher shades. They are used under the cheekbone, more dramatically than blushers, to give a hollow look.

Shaders and contours should never be used in soft, natural day make-up. They can be used to great effect for evening make-up and in photographic and fashion make-up. The key to successful application is a *very* light touch.

*Textures* Available as powder or cream. A good tip for a very natural look is to use two shades of foundation, darker for the natural contours of the cheekbones.

*'Tools' you need.* Contour brush.

**Mascara** This is used to emphasise eyes further by adding colour, thickness and sometimes length to lashes. It is most commonly available in a wand with its own brush applicator.

*Textures* There are waterproof mascaras which are oil-based to repel water. Some mascaras have tiny filaments which add thickness and length to lashes. Others do no more than add colour.

**Khol Pencil** These are always in dark colours and are used inside the rim of the eye to accentuate the white of the eye for a more dramatic effect. It is an exciting technique for night make-up. However, it should only be used along with a great deal of eye shadow or it will make the eyes appear smaller. Sharpen your Khol pencil in the same way as the eyeliner pencils.

**False Eyelashes** These are included here as

they can be a very effective and, at times, very necessary 'cosmetic'. There are strip lashes, which are a complete line of lashes; and single lashes which usually means three lashes on a strip together. It is rare to see false lashes work successfully as the usual method of applying them directly onto the eyelid looks very obvious, and invariably precarious!

## Foolproof Application Method for Strip Lashes

Top lid – draw a very thin line with liquid eyeliner next to the natural lashes. This provides a base for the strip. Use either a pin or cocktail stick and apply a little eyelash glue to this eyeliner line. Hold the false eyelash strip in its centre with a pair of tweezers and apply glue to the rim of the strip. The glue already applied to the eyelid

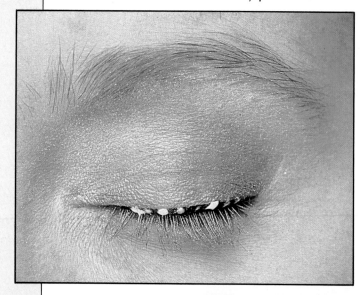

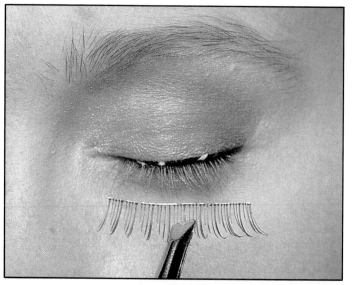

(Above) dots of eyelash glue along the base line of liquid eyeliner are now ready to accept the false eyelash strip. (Above right) eyelash strip held with tweezers and dotted with glue along its rim, ready to be applied to treated line on eyelid. (Right) a little practice will perfect this method and achieve a natural looking but glamorous set of lashes. (Opposite page) single lashes used at the outside corner of the eyes for a filmstar 'sweep'.

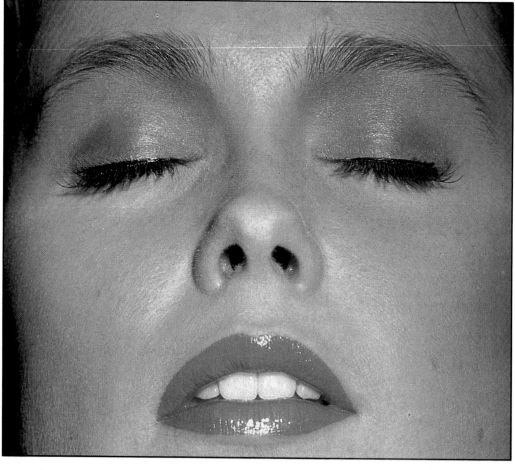

# Cosmetics and Textures

(Right) false eyelashes, properly applied (see page 24), can enhance a good eye make-up and give further versatility to your creativity. They are now available in different lengths and colours. (Far right) false eyelashes create the right 'weight' and texture, and offer contrast to this golden eye-shadow. Cosmetic colours and textures are now so varied that contrasting or toning to fashion fabrics and colours is

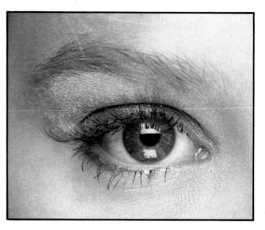

no longer a problem. (Above) bold, dynamic colours and glossy lipstick make full impact out of the drama of black. (Above right) the serenity of white is enhanced by using softer textures and paler colours in the make-up. (Opposite) the blue hat demands a positive response in make-up. Blue shadow and a sheen on the lips make the right impact.

will now be 'tacky' and ready to take the eyelash strip which will stick immediately. So, gently place the strip (still held by tweezers) on to the eyeliner line. Press the centre down first and then the ends.

Bottom lid – requires the same method but the false lashes are placed underneath the natural lashes. Apply glue only to the false lashes and not to the skin. Placing the false lashes underneath the real ones gives a natural hold which keeps them in place.
**Single Lashes** These are used at the

outside corner of the eye on top or bottom lid or both. They are attached to the natural lashes themselves and not to the skin. Hold the single lashes with a pair of tweezers and apply glue over them. Place these on top of the lashes on the top lid and press together.

Apply the false lashes underneath the real ones on the bottom lid.

False eyelashes are applied after all other make-up including mascara. A little practice will prefect this method, which gives a secure and natural-looking result.

# CHAPTER 2
# *Tools of the Trade*

(Right) correct pressure is all-important to successful application of make-up. This means a light touch, and use of the proper applicators. (Opposite page) it is worth investing in a set of real hair brushes as these are the most important 'tools' in your make-up kit.

There are many similarities between you and the artist who paints with oils. Before you can begin to work properly you have to be able to identify, understand and know how to use the 'tools of the trade': you must know about textures, what they do and how to apply them and match them for best results, and you must understand about colour, shade and light.

In fact, regard your face as the canvas for a painting. Make-up should lie on the surface of the skin as paint lies on the surface of a canvas. And because of this, the single most important factor in putting make-up on to the skin, is to apply the correct pressure. This means a touch light enough to apply the make-up successfully without encouraging the 'problems' of the skin type (e.g. dry or oily) to show on the surface of the skin. Use of the proper applicators and a full understanding of the capabilities of the different products helps considerably towards achieving the correct result.

**Brushes** These constitute the largest and most important section of your make-up 'tool kit'. The type and size that you choose affects the crucial factors of applying correct shape and pressure to the face.

If you can, invest in a set of real hair brushes as, with careful washing, they should never need replacing. Synthetic mixtures cost less but have a relatively short life. Sable has acquired a reputation as the best type of brush, but this has more to do with status than any practicality. In fact, sable is much too soft and pliable for proper application of face powder, blusher or contour. Any other type of real hair will do an excellent job – this could be pony, boar or kid!

The length of handle of a brush affects ease of working and effect of application. Different makes vary from 3" to as much as 10" and more. A sensible and comfortable length is about 5" as this gives a good balance when held in position. Brushes

over 6" in length may look impressive but do not do the job effectively. Equally, try to avoid the glamour of elaborate handles. These may look decorative on a dressing table but they become very cumbersome when held for any length of time.

Wash the brushes in mild soap. Rinse thoroughly in clean, warm water and pull bristles through your fingers to bring them tight together, (never leave hair splayed out when wet as this will ruin the shape). Leave to dry naturally. Never use artificial heat as this splits the hairs.

**A. Face Powder Brush** This is the largest brush as it covers the largest area (the entire face) and is not restricted to defining shape. A shorter haired brush would give a heavier, unacceptable dusting of powder to the skin.

**B. Blusher Brush** To apply blush powder to the cheekbones.

This looks very similar to the face powder brush but is slightly smaller as it has to work on the confined area of the

(Above) the blusher brush is smaller and more compact than the face powder brush. It has to work within the defined cheekbone area. (Top right) to apply liquid eye-liner, a very thin brush gives precision to a thin, straight line. (Bottom right) have tissues handy for blotting lips, to pat the face after spraying with Evian water (a fresh face), and to blot mascara if necessary. (Right) a dual-purpose eyebrow brush for applying colour to eyebrows, with miniature comb for separating eyelashes after applying mascara. (Opposite) this small-angled eye-shadow brush is a must if shadow is to be applied and blended within the curve of the socket line.

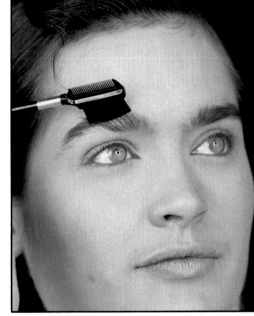

cheekbones. The importance of this slight size difference is demonstrated if you try to apply blusher to the correct area using a face powder brush. You will find it impossible to keep within the defined cheekbone area. If you have difficulty distinguishing between the two brushes you can simply label them.

**C. Contour Brush** To apply contour powder underneath the cheekbones. Also suitable for applying shaders around the face and for highlighting.

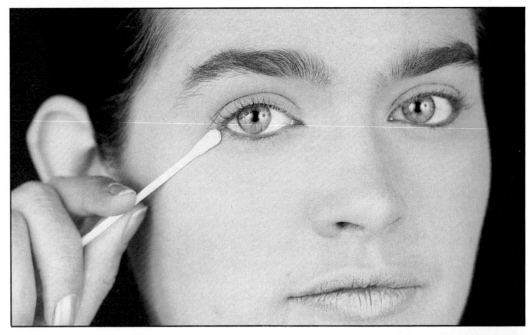

(Right) cotton buds will remove specks of stray make-up cleanly. Press, swivel and remove. (Below) a sponge-tipped applicator is the perfect 'tool' for blending loose and powder eye-shadow.

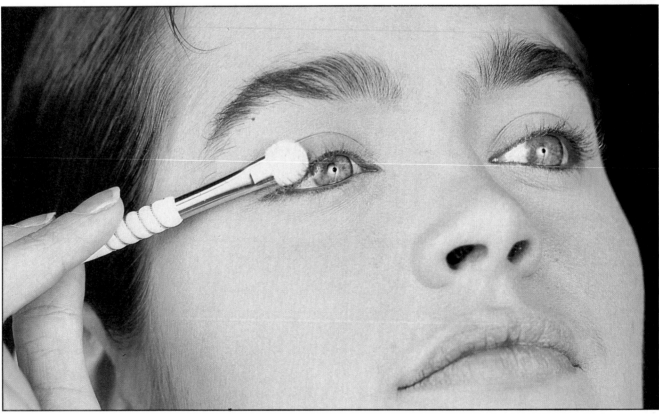

This brush is not good for blusher as it creates too much pressure on the skin. The hair should be very stiff, short and compact to give the required concentration of colour for its main task which is to contour the cheekbones.

**D. Eyebrow Brush** To apply shape and colour to the eyebrows.

This is like a miniature toothbrush and has short, stiff, nylon bristles. There are those which also have a miniature comb on the other side of the bristle head. This is useful dual-purpose tool as the comb can also be used to separate eyelashes, if necessary, after application of mascara.

**E. Eyeliner Brush** To apply liquid eyeliner or blend powder/pencil eyeliner along the rim of the eye.

A very thin-haired brush is needed to apply liquid eyeliner finely. A slightly thicker brush is necessary to blend powder or pencil eyeliner.

**F. Angled Eye Shadow Brush** To apply and blend powder eye shadow.

The angle of this brush is important. It allows you to follow and blend into the socket area quite easily. A straight brush makes it much more difficult to blend into the natural curve of the socket line.

Use an angled eyeliner brush to apply shadow successfully into the hollow of your eye.

**G. Fluff Brush** To 'finish off' blending of eye make-up.

This is the largest of the eye brushes. It is very soft so that it can be used over the finished eye make-up without disturbing the shapes but giving an overall softer look.

**H. Lip Brush** To apply lipstick and ensure a 'knife-edge' line to the lips.

The brush must have short, very thin bristles to make it flat. This gives a clean outline to the lips. Cut off any straggly hairs as the brush must be even for smooth application.

Non-brush 'tools' are equally important:

**Sponge-tipped Applicator** To apply and blend loose and powder eye shadow.

This really is essential as it is the perfect blending 'tool' for loose and powder eye shadow. It is also used to soften the harsh lines of an eyeliner pencil.

To clean, use a mild soap liquid and press sponge gently between finger tips,

being careful not to damage the hold of the plastic handle.

**Make-up Sponges** To blend foundation on the skin.

These come in a variety of shapes and sizes. Natural and synthetic sponges have to be moistened for use, which can cause problems of streaking. It is therefore very difficult to achieve a good result with this method unless you are very experienced.

The ideal make-up sponge is the latex rubber triangle or 'wedge'. This is used dry and therefore makes blending of foundation a relatively easy task for the beginner. Its wedge shape allows access to problem areas such as deep indentations around the nose, corner of the eye or middle of the chin. The 'wedge' has another, and very useful, function, which is a bonus of its rubbery texture. It can be used gently to erase mistakes. It takes off excess colour (e.g. too much blusher), shortens over-long lines around eyes, removes mascara or eye shadow which has fallen onto the cheekbones, and so on. In fact, your 'tool kit' would be sadly lacking without this 'Magic Wand'!

To clean use a mild soap liquid and squeeze gently.

Do not worry if stains remain on the sponge as these will in no way interfere with future application.

**Powder Puff (or cotton wool)** To apply loose face powder.

Either one of these is necessary to press (stipple) loose face powder onto the skin. The powder is not fine enough to be applied by brush. To clean a powder puff wash in a mild soap liquid (you can even put it in the washing machine!), and do clean it regularly or it will become increasingly difficult to deal with.

**Other Useful 'Tools'**

*Cotton Buds:* useful for removing 'stray' specks of make-up in awkward areas, e.g. mascara on top of cheekbones or browbone. Use point of cotton bud to press gently on area, swivel and remove.

*Evian Water Spray:* to freshen face before make-up.

*Tissues:* to press lips after lipstick application, and to 'pat' over face to remove excess moisture.

*Section Clips:* to keep hair away from face (and they cause minimum damage to a hair style).

*Eyebrow Tweezers:* to 'tidy-up' eyebrows.

# CHAPTER 3

# Preparation of the Skin

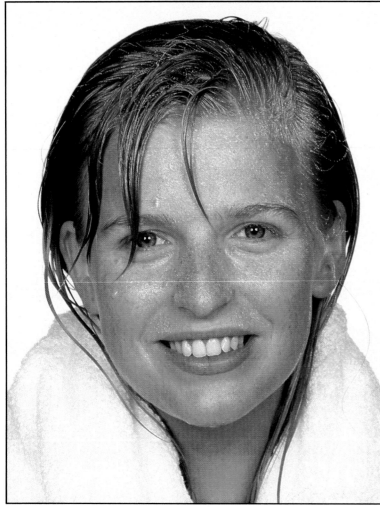

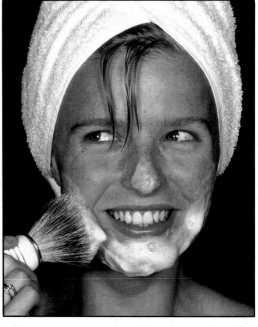

**Cleanse, Tone, Moisturise** A basic skin care routine of cleanse, tone and moisturise is the on-going preparation which contributes a great deal towards helping your skin look its best at all times. The action itself stimulates the skin and helps slough off the dead skin cells which lie on the surface and which can give your skin an unhealthy, dingy look. Ideally, you should cleanse, tone and moisturise morning and night and always before a make-up.

Keep your skin fresh and bright with regular cleansing to tone, and to slough off the dead skin cells which lie on the surface.

Preparation is boring! Yes, for the majority of us it surely is, but without it almost any job takes longer and the end result is usually far from satisfying. Applying cosmetics is no exception to the rule. Good preparation is absolutely essential to a perfect, finished make-up. You first have to create the correct surface to work on, and if this is done properly, even if you have an excessively dry or oily skin problem, this will not show through the finished make-up.

Regular cleaning helps to keep skin looking fresh and bright and is essential at the end of a day to clean away all the dirt that accumulates on the surface. Cream or lotion cleansers are specially formulated to dissolve make-up from the skin and are therefore very efficient. But soap and water is really just as effective and if this is the only way to make you skin feel fresh and clean, then go ahead. The only compromise that it is wise to suggest is to use a 'soapless' soap or a mild complexion bar. Ordinary soaps may be too highly perfumed or contain too harsh a detergent which will

(Opposite page) the majority of cleansers do an efficient job, so choose one that you're happy using. Gel cleansers are gentle to sensitive skins.

strip away too much of the skin's natural oils and so cause it to dry out. If you have a greasy or dry skin problem you could ask advice on special formulations from sales assistants; if you are allergy prone you may be wise to stay away from products containing lanolin or perfume.

Toners remove any left-over cleansing lotion and dirt and make you skin feel cool and fresh. Skin tonics or fresheners are the mildest and therefore the best. Astringents contain varying degrees of alcohol and are much harsher to the skin. They remove the skin's natural protective oil and can

Cleanse, tone and moisturise morning and night and always before a make-up.
Choose a skin tonic or freshener as the mildest form of toner. Astringents are harsh to the skin and remove its natural protective oil, so should only be used on very oily skins.

(Right) moisturising is an essential part of the skin care routine. It supports the skin's natural oils in creating a barrier against the damaging dryness of wind, sun and central heating. (Opposite page) spray over lightly moisturised face with Evian mineral water to achieve a fresh and 'neutral' base.

eventually make it dry and coarse. So, only use the latter, if you must, on very rare occasions as described in the 'Problems?' section.

Moisturising is the most important step in the cleanse, tone, moisturise routine. The skin is covered by its own natural moisturiser (a thin layer of oil called sebum) which helps to prevent excessive water loss. Use of a good 'artificial' moisturiser is extremely important as it acts as a further barrier between the skin and external drying elements such as wind, sun and central heating. This therefore doubles the effect of the skin's natural protection in keeping it supple and preventing it becoming too dry and thus more prone to wrinkling. Extra protection in sunshine is essential. Sunscreens which are water-resistant are the most effective, and of the moisturisers the water-in-oil preparations are the best (although they may be too 'oily' to wear under foundation). Ideally, you should use two types of moisturiser. A light consistency for daytime under make-up

(this must be light otherwise the make-up will slide), and a heavier one to 'feed' the skin at night. The latter is especially necessary to aid dry skin. Finding the right moisturiser for your skin is a matter of trial and error but once found (and used!) it can make a very positive contribution to the look of your skin.

**A Fresh Base** Before each make-up cleanse and tone to remove all make-up, surface film and excess oil as these affect application and finish of the make-up. Apply a light moisturiser over your freshly cleaned skin. As this stage you now have a 'neutral' surface and it is important to apply your foundation as quickly as possible for best results. First, however, spray over your moisturised face (fill a fine spray container with Evian mineral water) and blot well with a tissue, so that you have a fresh and 'neutral' base on which to start your make-up.

**Problems?** If you have skin which is too oily or dry extra steps can be taken to

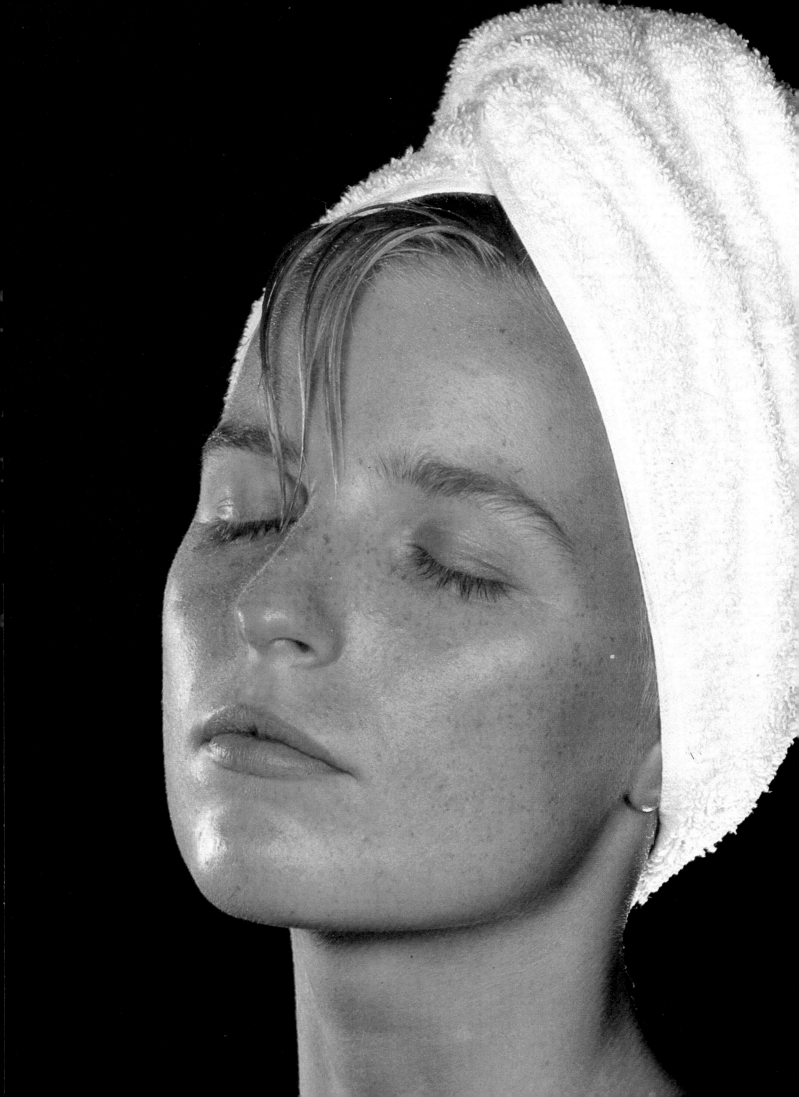

'neutralise' the surface so that these problems will not show through your foundation.

Dry skin is a particular problem as it does tend to show through make-up. Soak cotton wool in a strong (ie., high alcohol content) astringent and rub hard in circular motions all over your face. Any redness that occurs will fade quickly and meanwhile you will have created a smooth surface which will not flake through your finished make-up. However, this 'trick' should only be resorted to for very special occasions as over-use of astringents dries skin even more. Excessively oily skin makes foundation streaky and causes it to slide. The above method is equally successful in coping with this, and there is also a special film made by several cosmetic companies which is used on top of moisturiser as a sealant to stop the oil coming through. Otherwise, excess oil can be absorbed

(Above) to combat excessively oily or dry skin, use astringent to 'neutralise' surface before applying foundation. (Below right) pluck stray eyebrow hairs to ensure smooth blending of eye shadow, and to help towards a final, balanced look.

during the day by a light application of loose powder. If you only have slightly oily skin then blot your face with a tissue before using the Evian spray and then tissue off again after spraying.

Whichever technique you use always finish with a spray of Evian over the moisturiser and apply your foundation as quickly as possible while the surface of your skin is still 'neutral'.

**Eyebrows** Eyebrows must be smooth if your eye shadow is to blend perfectly, so pluck out any stray hairs. Tidy eyebrows also help towards the final balanced look.

# Day Make-Up

(Right) a fresh 'neutral' base ready to receive foundation and powder (and concealer where necessary). Perfect the art of applying foundation and powder as they provide the back-drop for the colour cosmetics. (Opposite page) a perfect, finished make-up which can only be achieved if the base of foundation and powder is successfully applied.

In many ways this is the most important chapter of the book, because all other forms of make-up are an extension of the subtle art of achieving a day-time look. The aim is to look as natural as possible in the harsh reality of daylight, and the general rule is that it is better to under- than over-make-up. It is always much easier to add more where needed than to take it away.

**Lighting** Before you begin it is important to arrange the best lighting possible. Ideally, your face should be lit from every angle so that there are no shadows to distort your judgement. A theatrical mirror (the type surrounded by small light bulbs) in a windowless room is perfect, but the least practical. In fact, any room with artificial light will do, so long as the entire room is lit. Natural daylight is the most difficult to work with as shadows are thrown onto the face, but the problems can be minimised if you sit with your back to the window.

**Concealer, Foundation and Powder** Having created the correct surface to work on, the next step is to apply your foundation and powder. This is a part of the make-up which has to be perfected. It provides the base for the colour cosmetics (blusher, eye shadow, etc) and if the backdrop isn't right then it is impossible to create a successful make-up.

It really cannot be said often enough that the single most important factor in successful application of make-up is the correct pressure. This means a positive but light touch which does not encourage the skin's problems to show through. This is particularly important in order to get an even finish with foundation, and this is considered elsewhere, but first you have to deal with those little imperfections.

**Spots, Blemishes and Other Imperfections** Take a good, honest look at your skin to assess your problems. All the very common imperfections such as broken veins, high cheek colour, dark areas (particularly under

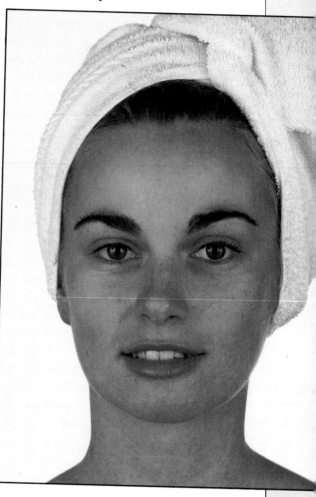

the eyes) and simple spots and blemishes can all be tackled successfully with clever concealing.

Concealers are generally applied before foundation, but can also be used on top of it. In either case it is most important to allow the concealer to become 'tacky' before blending, otherwise it will separate.

Water based concealers are best as these 'hold' to the skin and maintain coverage. An effective alternative to a general concealer is a cream foundation lighter in colour than the natural skin tone. This is not advisable for the older woman,

however, as the effect is not flattering.

Green cover sticks are popular for dealing with high cheek colour and broken veins. However, this is not a good idea if using liquid foundation, as a green tinge may show through the fine texture.

To use a concealer, take a small brush and apply it to the problem area, then press it onto the skin with a dry latex sponge. Pressing the concealer is far more efficient than blending, which will not always totally cover the flaw; the action of blending can also drag the delicate skin around the eyes.

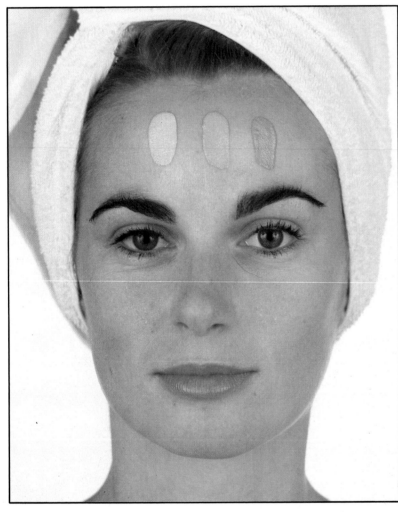

(Above) test for a foundation shade which matches your facial skin tone. (Opposite page) dot and blend foundation section by section. Blend with a dry latex sponge. Get rid of streaks with a one-inch flat brush worked left to right. Use a powder-puff to pat loose powder onto face.

*Foundation* If you apply too much pressure in the application of your foundation the mistake will be all too evident. It will stick to dry patches to give a heavy look; on oily patches the foundation will simply slide off, and on spots and other blemishes the make-up will appear 'caked'. The result is an unattractive and uneven finish. So avoid the heavy-handed approach at all costs!

*Types to use* There are two types of foundation. Oil-based, ideally only for use on dry, normal or combination skin, and water-based for oily skin. Water-based foundation dries very rapidly and therefore needs to be applied and blended fairly quickly to avoid a blotchy foundation colour.

You should always use a liquid foundation unless you have an especially difficult skin problem which requires extra coverage, in which case use a cream foundation.

*Choosing shade* Try to match the foundation shade (light, medium, dark) as closely as possible to your facial skin tone. There are no hard and fast rules as to where to test for this match. The back of the hand and the wrist are both used but are not ideal. Your forehead is the best testing ground (it is, after all, part of the face you are trying to tone with!) and is also the area used by cosmetic camouflage experts to achieve a near perfect result. If a good match has been made it will not be necessary to continue the foundation down the neck.

*Application* Foundation is applied to the face section by section, beginning with the forehead. Dot and blend each section before moving on to the next. A sensible route to follow is forehead, cheek, chin, cheek, nose and eyelids. If you dot your entire face with foundation some areas may dry before you are able to blend them, and this will create a very patchy finish.

To dot foundation use an eye shadow shading brush. This is a more effective applicator than your fingers, and makes filling-in difficult areas, such as deep indentations or the corners of the nose, much easier.

To blend foundation use a dry latex sponge for best results. Blend down the face to fade away under the chin. This downward action does not 'drag' the skin as you are simply gliding over the surface with gentle strokes. And, in blending down the face you work in the direction of the tiny facial hairs, which gives a smoother finish. If you blend upwards the facial hairs are ruffled and this makes it difficult to achieve a perfect result; also, any excess foundation will go into your hairline. Press rather than stroke the foundation onto red cheeks and other flaws as this method covers more effectively.

Eyelids should be covered with foundation to provide a good base for the eye make-up. It also blocks out veins and redness which tend to show on a fair skinned person, or the dark brown pigmentation that can be a problem with

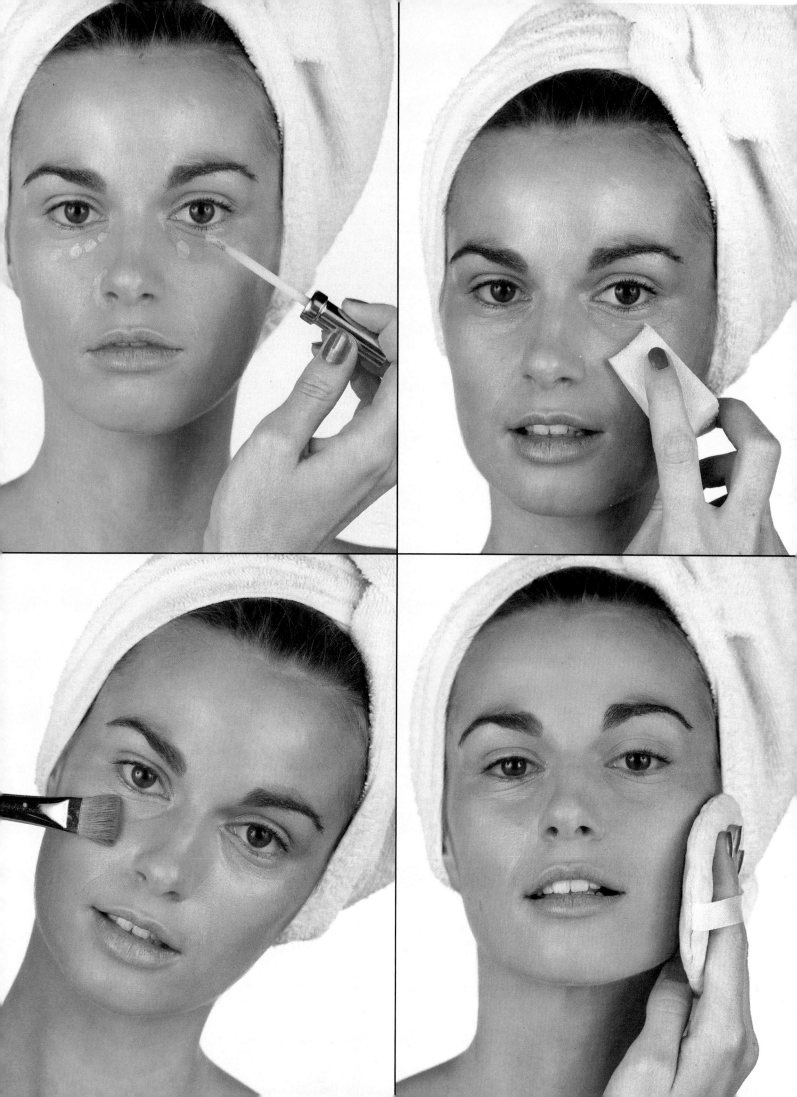

sallow skin. Do not apply too much foundation to the eyelids as this can cause eye shadow to crease. Gently lift eyebrow and blend foundation downwards towards the eyelashes.

Do not use foundation on deep lines, wrinkles or bags around the eyes as it will only accentuate these problems.

Lips are covered by foundation to give lipstick staying power and to prevent pigment in highly coloured lipstick staining the lips. Foundation should never be used to correct lip shape. This rarely works successfully and is, anyway, a very old fashioned technique.

If, when you have finished your careful application of foundation, you find that it looks streaky (usually because of oiliness) here is a foolproof tip. Take a large, flat, one inch brush and work over your face very lightly from left to right and all the streaks will disappear.

**Face Powder** Face Powder is used to 'set' foundation to make sure that it lasts all day or all night. Translucent is the most popular powder as it allows the natural skin tone to glow through.

*Types to use* If you use a liquid foundation then 'set' it with a block powder. Always use the combination of liquid foundation and block powder when you can as they give the finest finish. But remember that you can use loose powder instead of block if you have a very oily skin, as this will help absorption.

If you use a cream foundation you must 'set' it with loose powder to ensure that it lasts over a long period of time.

*Application* To apply block powder use a face powder brush and stroke it onto your face. Work downwards only (in the direction of facial hairs). Continue until skin is smooth and silky to touch.

To apply loose powder use cotton wool balls or a powder puff. Press the powder on to your skin patch by patch so that you do not 'drag' the foundation. This pressing action also helps absorb excess oil.

Don't be shy of applying powder (although more caution is needed with loose). To test that the foundation is well covered place the back of your hand against different areas of your face. If the skin is sticky or clammy to the touch more powder is needed.

Have faith if the initial powdering looks rather heavy, as this is put into perspective when the make-up is complete; also some of the powder is absorbed by your foundation.

Eyelids are also powdered and these are 'set' against the creases. Lift your eyebrow gently to stretch the eyelid. Blend away foundation creases and then apply powder down towards the eyelashes. If you do not first blend the foundation creases away and if you apply powder from the eyelashes up, then you simply 'set' these creases. This means that the eye shadow will crease when you apply it.

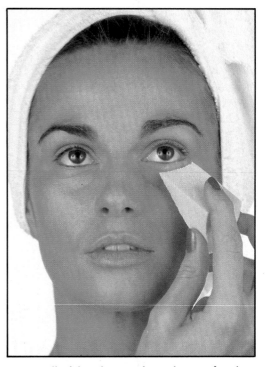

Finally, blend away foundation that has creased in the under-eye area. Dip the tip of your 'wedge' sponge into the face powder and 'set' up to your lashes. Do not use a brush for this area as it will irritate your eyes.

*Quick Guide to Foundation and Powder Matches in Day or Evening Make-Up*

Liquid Foundation – Translucent Block Powder

Cream Foundation – Translucent Loose Powder

Gels – Translucent Block or Loose Powder

Problem skin (too bad to be evened out by Concealer and Liquid Foundation) – Cream Foundation and Loose Powder

Very Oily Skin (with no major flaw problems) – Liquid Foundation and Loose Powder

Cream Eye Shadows and Cream Blushers – 'Setting' with face powder

(Right) 'setting' foundation in under-eye area. A brush would irritate the eyes. (Opposite page) use of a thin-handled brush along the cheek helps to define angle and area for blusher application.

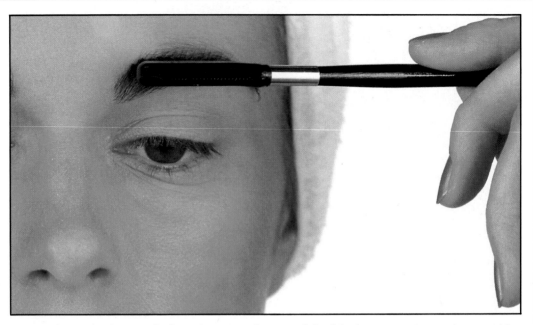

(Right) hold eyebrow brush horizontally to follow line of eyebrows. (Opposite page) alternative applicator, the eyebrow pencil being held in correct position to achieve a soft effect.

Concealer – Only needed under Liquid Foundation

**Blusher** If you apply your blusher at this early stage it helps give shape to the face and this makes it easier for you to decide on the correct eye make-up. The purpose of a blusher is to accentuate bone structure and to add colour to the face. It is an area of make-up that has become greatly over-complicated and you will not find in this section the normal array of diagrams showing individual techniques for triangle and pearshaped faces! The guidelines for application given here work equally successfuly on any shape of face and are also easy to relate to our three dimensional reality. But first you have to select the correct blusher for the job.

*Types* Powder blusher should ideally be used for day make-up. It is the finest textured of all, and as it is applied with a brush you have more control when shaping.

If you use a cream blusher it must be applied before the face powder. As with all creams, it needs to be set by the powder to stop it creasing later on.

There are light coloured blushers in pale pink or peachy shades, and dark coloured blushers. They both serve to make the cheek bones more prominent, but work in opposite ways. The light blushers act as highlighters and are applied along the cheekbones. The dark blushers make areas recede and are applied below the cheekbones.

Note: highlighters and shaders must never be used in day make-up as their effect is too dramatic and unnatural. Skilled use of the blusher cancels out the need for highlighters and shaders.

*Where to apply* Blusher must be kept within strict confines for a day look or the result will be ridiculous.

**1.** First you have to pinpoint the cheekbone. Take an imaginary line from the bulbous piece at the entrance to your ear down to the corner of your mouth. Placing a thin handled brush across the cheek helps define the angle.

Light blushers are applied 2" up from this line

Dark blushers are applied 1" up from this line

**2.** Do not apply blusher any lower down the cheekbone than the end of your nose, (imagine a diagonal line drawn from the tip of your nose across your cheek).

**3.** Do not apply blusher any closer to the centre of your face than the outer corner of your eye, (imagine a line, from the outer corner down your cheek to meet the imaginary nose line).

**4.** Do not apply blusher any higher than the temple.

*How to apply* Use a very light touch as too much pressure gives a blotchy, 'clown-like' appearance.

Always start at the hairline. Eighty percent of the blusher will come off at first point of contact giving a high density of colour. The centre of the face cannot take this, whereas the hair line can.

Work down the face with short strokes in the direction of the facial hair, gradually fading blusher away at the correct point. If blusher application is blotchy, finish off with face powder.

**Eyebrows** Eyebrows frame the eyes and affect the total look. They should therefore be worked on before you apply eye shadow. The object, as with all make-up, is to improve upon your natural features, so do not falsify your normal eyebrow shape.

Use a pencil, or a powdered shadow which you apply with a short, stiff nylon brush. In both cases colour is delicately and gradually put on to the eyebrow with short strokes. To soften a hard pencil line use the eyebrow brush.

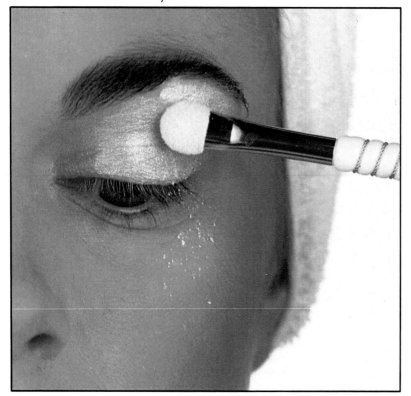

(Above) always start with lightest colour. (Opposite page, top left to right) application of darkest eye colour. Harsh pencil lines are blended with sponge-tipped applicator. Colour 3 shows contrast and application. Colour 4 defines the shape of the eye.

Pencils are slightly more difficult to use than shadows. If too much pressure is applied you will create a hard line which will look false. The 'trick' is to hold the pencil between your thumb and first finger, very close to its unsharpened end so that it is held in a straight line which could continue up to the ceiling. In this way you will find it impossible to put any pressure on the eyebrow and will easily achieve a soft effect.

If your eyebrows are a little sparse or the hair colour fair, very gently colour the hairs that are there. By this careful action you will also mark the skin itself in a very natural way. This is called 'feathering in'. Hold the pencil as in the photograph but even lower down the stem.

**Eye Shadow** Most eye make-up guides, like face shape guides for blusher, confuse by presenting an array of different shapes with

diagrams for specific make-up. The first problem is in identifying the correct shape before you can begin work! Here is a basic shading technique which, with slight variations, will suit everybody. Four contrasting colours are required, and you can use any of the eye shadow textures, but for the ultimate smooth, soft day look loose or cream powder eye shadow gives the best results.

**Colour 1.** This is the lightest of the four colours you apply to the eye. Its purpose is to highlight the browbone and to give a base to the other colours.

Gently stretch your eyelid by placing a finger just above the eyebrow, next to the temple, and lift. Apply shadow just below your eyebrow and blend down towards the eyelashes. Cover the entire eyelid. Fade away all colour: pay special attention to the corner of your eye, where harsh lines can form.

**Colour 2.** This is the darkest of the colours you choose and is applied with a pencil under the bottom lid and over part of the top lid. Its purpose is to accentuate the eye. An eye pencil gives the control necessary to draw in the lines successfully.

Gently place a finger against the outside corner of your eye to keep the skin tight and get rid of creases. This enables you to draw a solid, straight line close to the rim of the eye. Begin at the outside corner of your eye as this is the thickest part and can therefore take the extra concentration of colour. Draw a line about three quarters of the way along the bottom lid, fading colour away towards the nose.

Draw a line along the top lid to a point just beyond the outer edge of the iris of your eye. This line is much thicker than that on the bottom lid and is extended into a triangle shape.

Blend the pencil lines with a sponge-tipped applicator for a soft, natural look.

Used correctly a pencil will not drag the delicate skin around the eyes.

**Colour 3.** The third colour fills the area from the beginning of the eyebrow down to the inside corner of the eye. It is darker than the base colour, lighter than the pencil, and contrasts with the fourth colour. Its purpose is two-fold. It gives a soft but greater definition to the nose, making the overall look much sharper, and it also makes the eyes appear larger.

Start at the beginning of the eyebrow and blend colour down the line of your nose and in towards the corner of your eye.

**Colour 4.** The fourth colour is the most important as it defines the shape of the eye.

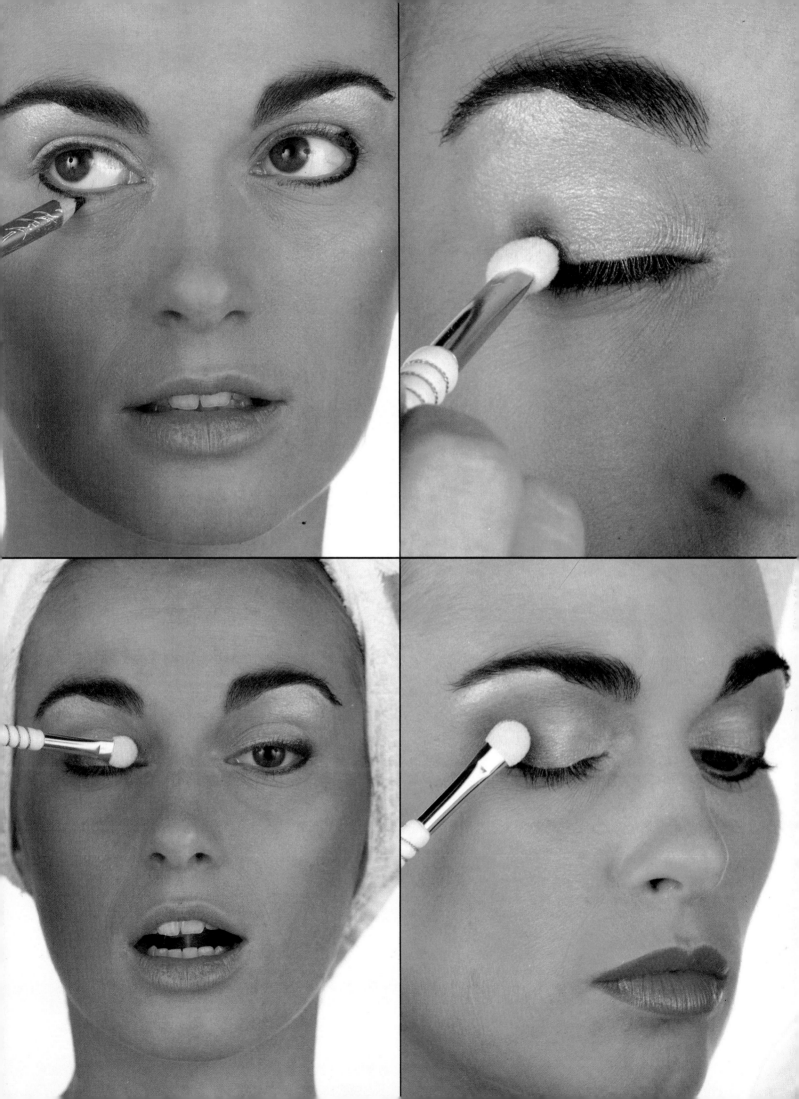

It should contrast with the third colour but still be lighter than the pencil colour.

Before applying the fourth eye shadow colour you have to decide on the shape it should take. This can only be properly decided by looking at a visually balanced face. So it is wise at this stage to put on your lipstick (technique explained in Lipstick section).

Apply the eye shadow to the top lid over the area covered by the eye pencil, next to your eyelashes. Most of the eye shadow colour will be unloaded at this point.

(Above) a lip brush gives a clean line. Lay it flat against the lips and follow the natural outline. (Opposite) when mouth has been contoured, fill in where necessary.

Blend the shadow with downward strokes, but work up over the pencil area towards the eyebrow. The decision as to how high to take this colour is determined by the degree of your socket line when your eyes are open. If you have no visible socket line blend the colour higher towards the eyebrow. If you have a large socket area blend the colour slightly lower. In both cases the shape of the eye shadow should be soft and rounded; it should not be extended beyond the natural eye socket area in a dramatic, winged effect.

You take this colour across the browbone to blend with the nose line

colour for the finished effect. But keep checking the shape you are creating throughout your application of this fourth colour. The finished shape should be soft and rounded, and should not extend towards the temple in a winged effect.

*Why this technique is special* The usual method of applying eye shadow is to take it right across the eyelid following the socket line. This makes the face appear broader and the eyes seem smaller. The illusion is similar to that created when a plump person wears a dress with horizontal stripes; it makes her look much bigger than she actually is. The special technique described above keeps the face in proportion and makes the eyes appear larger. What is more, the effect can be used successfully, with slight variations of eye shadow shape, on every type of eye.

**Lipstick** Choose a lipstick colour which tones with your blusher. This gives a well co-ordinated effect.

Apply lipstick with a lip brush for a knife-edge line. You can use a lip pencil but it is more difficult to achieve a sharp outline; however, colour can be taken off the pencil with a lip brush.

Lips must be closed to give a firm surface. Take plenty of lipstick on to the brush (this makes it easier to achieve a good line). Lay the brush flat against your lips and move evenly along following the natural outline. When the mouth has been contoured in this way, fill in where necessary. You will have to open your lips to colour the corners of your mouth properly.

Now blot the lipstick by placing an open tissue full against your mouth and, using the flat of your thumb, press the tissue over your lips. Be careful here not to apply too much pressure or you will take off too much of your lipstick.

If you see a need to accentuate your lips, outline the bow of the top lip with a fine lip pencil and blend with a lip brush.

To give lipstick extra staying power blot with a tissue and dust with loose powder before applying a second coat. And, for a soft, dewy look, finish off with a little lip gloss, (but do not take this to the edges of your mouth as it may cause the lipstick to run).

**Mascara** This is the final stage to your make-up and one of the most flattering of all cosmetics. Even the loveliest of lashes can be further enhanced and glamorised by a coating of mascara.

Look down into your mirror and begin

(Above) the tip of the mascara wand successfully coats lower lashes. (Opposite) delicate use of blusher on chin, nose and forehead to finish off with a warm glow.

application on the top side of the top lashes to deposit most of the mascara here. This also takes off any powder that has dropped from the eye shadow. Now look up and finish off the top lashes with a coating from underneath. Use the point of the mascara wand (brush) to coat your bottom lashes.

Use a tissue to remove excess mascara from the wand (brush) to avoid clogging your lashes. If, despite precautions, the lashes do become clogged, place a tissue underneath your open eye, close your eye, and comb lashes with an eyebrow brush. To remove specks of mascara from your cheek take a cotton bud and lightly swivel on the mascara speck and remove.

There are lots of lovely mascara colours to choose from these days so it is worth indulging to make your eye make-up even more attractive.

**The Finishing Touch** To complete your daytime make-up add finishing touches with blusher on chin, nose and forehead. This helps towards a warm, delicate glow.

# Day Make-Up

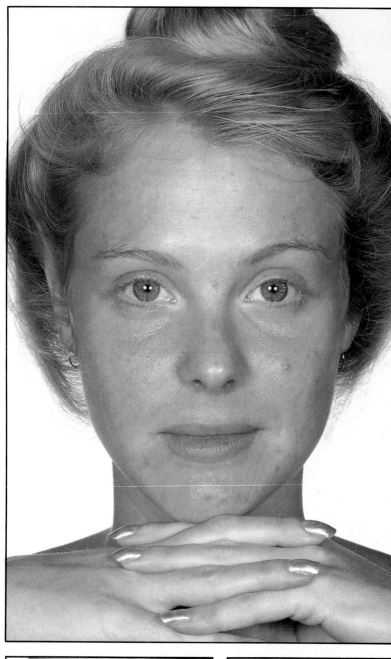

(Left) the bare canvas, in need of clever concealing work, foundation and powder. (Below) blusher applied in the early stages gives shape to your face and helps to create a balanced eye make-up. (Bottom left to right) the four basic steps to eye make-up shape and colour, when successfully mastered, can be adapted by you to suit any mood and occasion. Lips can be painted to perfection with the precision of a lip brush. Add lashings of mascara for the final, glamorous touch. (Opposite) the total transformation to a soft, glowing and natural day look.

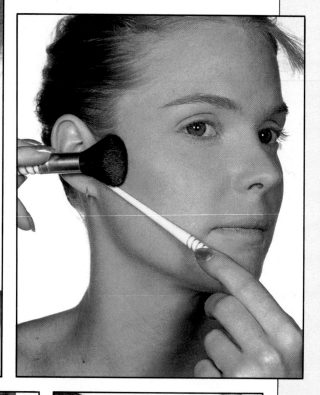

# CHAPTER 5

# *Evening Make-Up*

(Right) bold lips and subtle but effective use of frosted eyeshadow and false lashes for a truly glamorous evening look. (Opposite) a softer approach, but equally stunning especially in candlelight! (Overleaf) dramatic use of shading and blusher around the eyes for a devastating, smouldering effect. Close-up on facing page.

Evening make-up need not be any different from day make-up. But the more flattering quality of night lighting and the mood set by glamorous evening fashions gives you licence to be more adventurous.

The general rule about evening make-up is that it requires a heavier application to ensure that facial features and make-up colours stand out in some of the more dimly lit night-time settings. It is, in fact, an exaggerated form of day make-up, but with a wider choice of colours (mixing natural and synthetic) and the use of more dramatic shapes and textures.

**Foundation and Powder** Evening make-up is generally put more to the test than day make-up. For instance, to withstand a night of dancing and some perspiration it is crucial that the base is dependable.

So, for the more demanding occasions, use a cream foundation and 'set' with a light

**1.** Take the light coloured blusher (the one that is applied *on* the cheekbone) up onto the temple and/or forehead. You can even take it over the entire eye area using it as your base eye shadow colour. Or, bring the blusher round into the eye area and blend with your base colour.

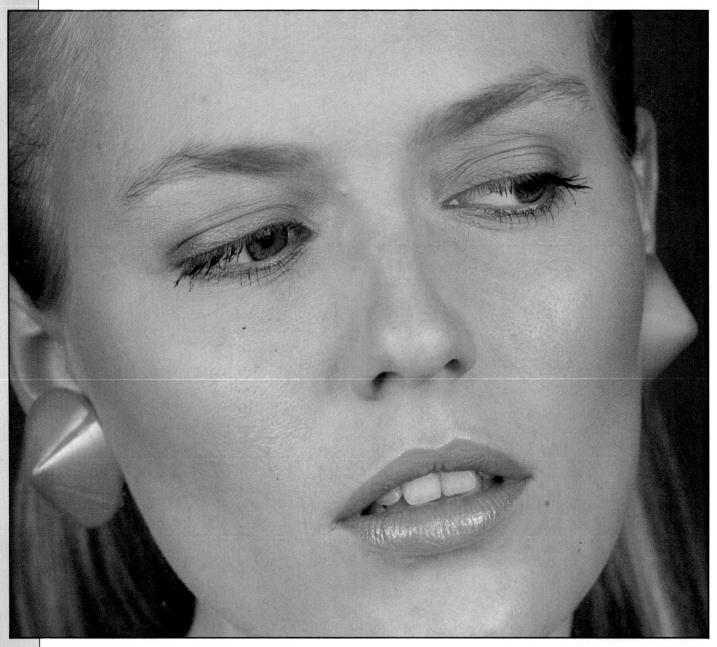

(Above) for frivolous party mood the 'synthetic' look (e.g. pinks, lilacs etc.) and (opposite) matched to an outfit, creates the ultimate in total co-ordination.

application of loose powder. This heavier finish means the base is less likely to 'move' during the evening.

For extra glamour substitute translucent face powder for one with a gold, bronze or frosted tint.

**Blusher** There are two ways to create an attractive and dramatic effect with your blushers.

**2.** Apply dark blusher to the underside of the cheekbone for a 'model girl' look.

**Contouring** For a really dramatic look, shade under the cheekbone. But only a young person can get away with this rather theatrical effect. You can use either a contour (underneath the cheekbone) with a dark blusher as second colour, or choose two shades of blusher in pink and plum.

The technique is the same as that described for blushers.

Dark shade, only about ¼ inch in width.
Lighter shade, about ¾ inch in width.

**Eye Shadow** Colours can be darker than those for day eye shadows, but the colour graduation remains the same (i.e. base is lightest, eyeliner darkest, nose line and fourth colour to contrast with each other. Here are some suggestions for a good evening look.

**Colour 1.** Instead of a base white use a colour. This cancels the need for colour three (the nose line) as the base colour now introduces the definition and slimming effect in this area. If you do use white as a base then the other three colours must be darker than for a day time look or they will not stand out enough.

**Colour 2.** Blend the pencil with the eyebrow (stiff, nylon) brush instead of a sponge tipped applicator to keep the line more dramatic.

Almost anything goes in evening make-up. Use gold eye-shadow everywhere. On lips, eyes, cheeks and even to highlight other lipsticks.

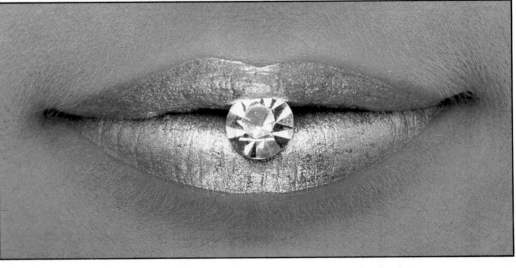

**Colour 3.** The same area as for day make-up is covered. However, if you use a colour for the base this step will not be necessary.

**Colour 4.** The same technique as for day make-up but create a different shape. Take the colour higher towards the eyebrow and sweep it outwards to make a pointed (winged) rather than a rounded effect.

**Khol** A wonderful way to exaggerate and enlarge the eyes. But only use khol pencil along with lots of eye shadow, otherwise it will have the opposite effect and make your eyes appear smaller.

Apply khol all around the inside rim of the eye. Use the same technique of application as for ordinary eyeliner.

**Lipstick** The colour of the lipstick must balance out eye and blusher colours. So, if

The before and after of an evening make-up. Bold use of colour linked to outfit, and bold use of blusher and highlighter for a sparkling effect.

Heavy use of a colour eyeshadow all round the eyes, and basic day look techniques adapted for a touch of drama.

darker colours have been used, the lipstick should also be a dark shade. Add plenty of gloss for a glamorous evening look.

**Lip Liner** A more dramatic evening look can take the boldness of a lip liner. This is applied before the lipstick. You can draw directly onto the lips or take the colour off the pencil with a lip brush. Alternatively, you can use a darker colour lipstick than the one you use to fill in the lips. In either case, simply trace the outside line of your mouth.

**Mascara** Choose a coloured mascara rather than black or brown to further complement night eyes. Apply more than for a day look to give extra emphasis and also because you have to contrast against darker eye shadows.

**False Lashes** These can really come into their own in an evening make-up. Apply three or four single lashes to the outer edge of the top lid for a sweeping effect. Or, apply full strips to top and bottom lids.

**Highlighting** As a finishing touch use a highlighter to give a general 'lift' to your face. The browbone, top of the cheekbone underneath the eye, centre panel of nose, and lower cheek following the jaw bone,

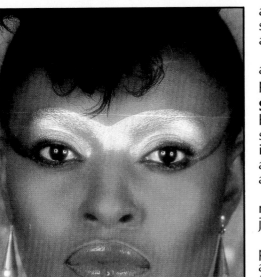

are the usual areas. This can only be successful with a very light touch and "careful blending.

Highlighting must never be obvious, and plenty of practice is necessary to perfect this most subtle of techniques.

**Shading** As subtle a technique as highlighting, and equally difficult to achieve successfully, shading should only be used in evening make-up (daylight makes it almost impossible to 'hide' the shaded areas), and only if you are quite young.

The main reasons a shader may be necessary are to slim down a nose or jawbone.

As this technique is the most difficult part of any make-up, the easiest way to attempt it is to use a shade darker in foundation in the areas above applied with your main foundation colour.

Remember any obvious shadow line will be concealed by the application of powder.

Use of theatrical make-up enables you to be daring and creative. Black skins complement frosted and synthetic colours beautifully. They can also take dramatic use of contours and highlighting in the evening.

# CHAPTER 6

## Colour in Make-Up

Matching, toning, co-ordinating, contrasting. These are words so commonly used in connection with colour and which terrify so many people. The fashion houses long ago began to break all the colour rules which many of us held sacrosanct – 'blue and green should never be seen' – leaving the less confident of us really in a sea of colour! But understanding colour and how to use it in the art of make-up is really quite straightforward, and it is important to grasp it if you are to achieve the ultimate of total colour co-ordination between your make-up and clothes.

(Left) the synthetic colours of pinks, blues, lilacs, purples. (Above) a completely natural look using only earth and autumnal colours.

# Colour in Make-Up

The only colours which are included in both the 'natural' and 'synthetic' colour categories are white, black and red.

Colours fall into two categories. The naturals, which comprise all the earth and autumnal colours, and the synthetics, which comprise every other colour known to make-up e.g. pink, lilac, purple, etc. The only colours which are included in both categories are white, black and red. Simply, the guidelines are, for a day make-up keep to one or the other colour category and you will always achieve a good, co-

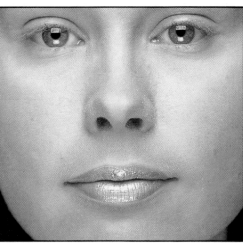

A beautiful, muted effect using 'synthetic' colours on lips and cheeks. Ideal for daytime, goes with any outfit, and is quick to apply.

ordinated look; for an evening occasion you can afford to mix the two categories for a more exciting, vibrant effect.

**The Muted Look** With this technique the colour you choose for your cheeks and lips dictates whether the overall colour effect is natural or synthetic. The art is to use just two muted, neutral shades on your eyes, which are able to adapt to or 'reflect' the stronger tones of the blusher and lipstick. So, for example, a white eye shadow covers the entire eyebrow and lid while the second colour, say grey, outlines the outside corner of the eye and smudges up slightly onto the lid. You can now choose either synthetic colours (e.g. pink lipstick

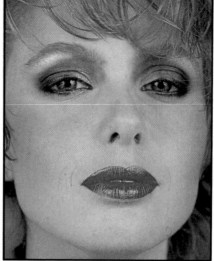

and plum blusher) or natural colours (eg., coral peach lips and a rusty, coppery blusher) and either combination will work equally successfully with the soft, neutral eye shadows.

The technique has many advantages. It lessens the confusing choice of up to four different eye shadow colours. It solves the problems of co-ordinating with an outfit as you cannot really go wrong with this method. And, possibly most important, it is very time-saving on a busy morning!

**Complexion, Hair and Eyes** There is much nonsense spoken about matching make-up colours and general complexion. Here are some simple and effective guidelines.

*Eyes.* Any colour of eye make-up should work with any shade of eye. If it does not, it usually means that it has been

applied too strongly. In which case, it can be softened down in stages if you dust translucent block powder on top until the right depth is achieved.

*Hair.* The only hair colour that can cause real problems is red, although this caution applies more as a person becomes older.

*Skin.* Pale skin, no matter what the colour of hair, is best complemented by synthetic colours. Sallow skin, or a skin that has a tan, is more suited to the natural colours.

Above all, your use of colour should be fun, imaginative and versatile within the given guidelines. Suntans disappear, seasons change and so do fashions, and in order to keep up with this constantly changing scene you have to adapt your choice of make-up colours to suit the mood.

(Below) 'natural' make-up, again using earth and autumnal colours. (Opposite) use of 'synthetic' colours. (Overleaf) the muted look.

# CHAPTER 7

# Disco and Elaborate Evening

Use frosted make-up, mix colours that spark your imagination, paint on marks (opposite and overleaf). Match lips to eyeshadows outrageously; be pale and interesting but make the lips bold (subsequent pages). Use your cosmetics as a paint box, for now is the time to be really creative.

Now you have mastered the basics of the art of make-up you can really enter into the world of art if you so desire. Fancy dress, disco, almost any special occasion gives you licence to be free and easy with your imagination. Be exotic, mysterious, fantastical, frightening – but above all, have fun.

# Fashion Make-Up

(This page and opposite) Spring and Summer for softer and bolder use of seasonal colours. (Overleaf) for an autumn woolly, autumn make-up colours; and a strong, frosted eye make-up makes a pale winter face more interesting.

A 'fashion look', whether it be in clothes, make-up or hair, is a style of the moment. The 'moment' can last from months to years. And these 'styles', 'fashions', 'looks', are mainly inspired by the famous names on designer clothes labels and by the great fashion houses. A popular style of clothing, for instance, can encourage famous hair salons to create a complementary hairstyle; and the colours adopted as fashionable for the various designer clothes collections dictate the make-up colours through each season.

In America, the ultimate fashion look is total co-ordination of a person's make-up and clothes' colours. Certainly, make-up

# Fashion Make-Up

suld always reflect or match the mood of an outfit. A dress which is bold in style or colour should be matched in impact by the make-up and, if the dress is softer in style and colour, the make-up follows suit. The most dramatic changes of colour are seen from season to season. Autumn and winter fashion colours tend to be darker and heavier; stronger make-up colours reflect this and better compliment a pale, winter face. In spring and summer the brighter colours appear, along with pastels, whites and neutrals. Make-up therefore should be softer and lighter, both in colour and application. Also, the more colourful warm weather complexions and tans are more in harmony with the 'natural' outdoors look.

Make-up should reflect the mood of an outfit for a complete fashion look. (Opposite) this soft, glowing, natural look is ideal for the softer fabrics and styles of spring and summer fashions.

More dramatic use of colour and technique to complement bolder fashion colours and styles.

# Model Make-Up

A combination of photogenic features and clever use of cosmetics and techniques can transform a model girl into a multitude of different people. Look at these photographs and those on the next four pages for an idea of the clever use of make-up combined with photographic and fashion skills in creating a total 'look'.

Make-up can give you confidence, but first you must have confidence in it. Confidence in its power to project and enhance for you; even to change your image completely if that's what you want. The most potent example of the use of make-up is in the world of commercial photography. Make-up is expertly applied to a model specifically to help create the right 'image' for a product or company. It may have to be

Some very different make-ups created by experts to adapt a model's features to the mood of the message or product that she is to 'promote' on the magazine pages. See also overleaf.

sophisticated, futuristic, old-fashioned or girl-next-door. And the majority of photographic models can be adapted with the use of make-up to all four looks. Thumb through a model's portfolio of photographs and it is very difficult to believe that it is the same girl in every shot.

It may also be hard for you to believe that many models are quite ordinary to look at in the 'flesh' but, with their photogenic features and the magic of make-up, they can turn into beautiful, sophisticated women on the fashion pages.

# Make-Up for Coloured Skin

Black skin complements both 'synthetic' and 'natural' colour. The most stunning effects can be created with frosted products (this page and opposite).

The shade of a black skin can range from beautiful mahogany to ebony black. Today there are an increasing number of products specially formulated for black skins. This is important as cosmetics designed for white skins tend to change colour when applied to a black skin. Foundations and powders, for instance, can turn greyish, or too red or yellow. If you are lucky, a bronzing gel or tinted moisturiser might be enough to protect and to even out skin tone. However, black or white, a complexion will almost always benefit from the classic base of concealer, foundation and powder.

**Concealer, Foundation, Face Powder** The techniques are the same as for day make-up for a white skin, but, if you prefer, you can substitute the concealer with a foundation lighter in shade than your all over base shade. Always apply concealer/foundation before your base foundation.

Foundations for black skins are oil-based, but less so than for white skins. This off-sets problems of dryness without adding unnecessarily to oiliness. Choose your shade of foundation, i.e. light, medium or dark, to match skin tones. Follow the basic rules for powder but do not over-do the initial application. White skins can take a heavy, one-off setting over foundation, but on a black skin too much powder looks obvious and greyish. It is, therefore, far better to 'set' a couple of times throughout the day and also to apply with a brush as this helps avoid a heavy look.

**Shading and Shaping** These techniques can be very successful on a black skin for day make-up as the contrast to skin tone is very subtle. For best results use a sheer, liquid foundation which is darker than your base. This could mean a very dark brown or nearly black foundation colour for an extremely dark skin. Shade down sides of nose, along jawline, under the cheekbone and inside the eye-socket area. Of course, if you do use a foundation as shader you

Black skins tend to be oily, although if exposed to cold weather they can also suffer from dryness, and so require the protection of moisturisers. It is therefore most important to find the right base and, if this oily-dry combination is a problem, time spent on researching a suitable foundation formulation will pay dividends.

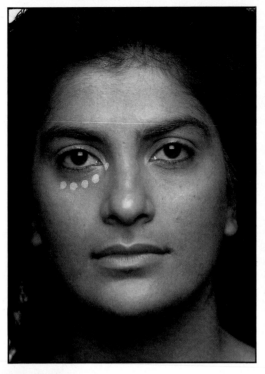

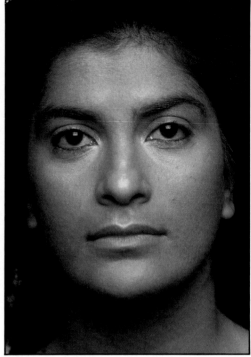

Highlighter dotted along top of cheekbone and blended in, works beautifully on this lovely Indian skin tone. (Below) full use of vibrant 'synthetic' colours gives this skin tone a stunning effect and contrasts with jet-black hair and the boldness of black leather. (Opposite page) an Indian wedding make-up. Vivid colours with a creative design around the cheekbones and eyes match the shimmering, exciting colours of the outfit to the full. Kohl pencil is used to emphasise and dramatise the beautiful eyes, while bold, red lips balance the make-up and match the boldness of the rich fashion colours.

must 'set' with powder after its application on top of the base so that both are secure.

**Blushers and Highlighters** The same methods are used as for white skin. But choose non-greasy, creamy blushers or gels. Avoid powder blushers especially if you have undue oiliness.

Highlighters can be very effective. Try a light dusting down the bridge of the nose, around the eye area, above cheekbones and just above the upper lip.

**Eye Shadow** Bright, vivid colours look best on black skins, although day make-up will always look softer than on a white skin as there is less contrast for colour. Do not be tempted to apply more colour to obtain contrast as this will look unattractive in daylight. Obviously, for evening eyes you can use extra colour, and golds, coppers and frosted shadows look very good. These can even be dusted around the face for a more exotic effect.

Follow the same format for making-up eyes as described in the appropriate chapter, along with the following thoughts:

**1.** A white base is too dramatic against a black skin. Choose a colour or leave natural skin tone as base.

**2.** Although black or brown can be used to effect as an eyeliner, you could also try navy blue.

**3.** Take care to choose a colour prominent enough to outline the nose.

You may be lucky enough to have a natural khol effect around your eyes.

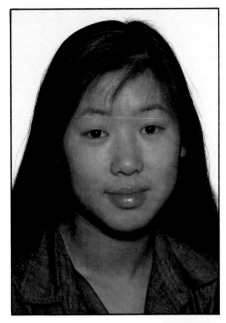

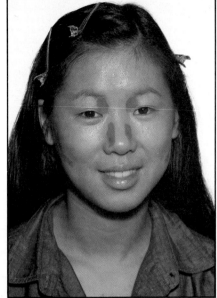

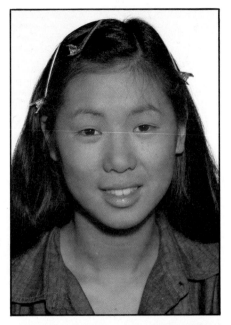

As a shading technique on a darker skin, use a foundation colour darker than the base. Apply down sides of nose, along jawline and under cheekbones. Highlighters can be very effective also (above centre, above right). (Right) to create a socket line use light shadow next to lashes, and darker shadow on the outer corner of eye. (Opposite) bright, vivid colours and frosts can be used to great effect.

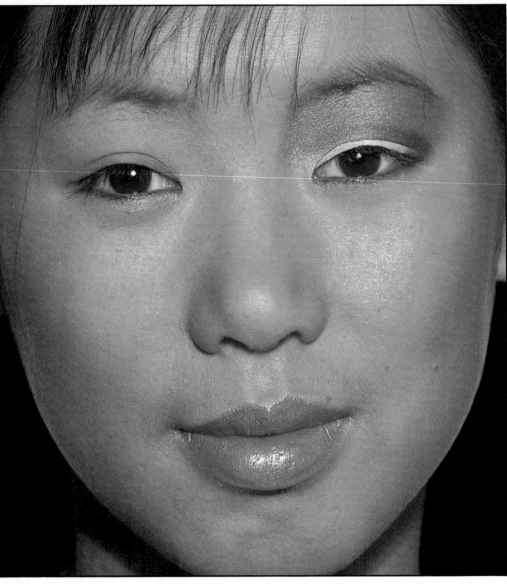

(Right) dramatic use of foundation and powder emphasise the pretty mouth and eyes of this Oriental girl. (Opposite) full make-up with use of blusher, highlighter and frosted eye-shadow for a glossy evening look.

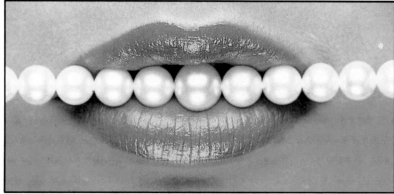

Experiment with using a colour over this if you think it will better complement you make-up. And if you do not have this natural effect then introduce it using lots of black or other suitable colour.

**Lipstick** Many black women have ample and beautifully formed lips which do not need exaggerating. But if you wish to slim your lips then trace the outline with a dark brown or black lip pencil and fill in with lipstick. To soften the outline apply foundation over the top, and powder to set.

# CHAPTER 11

# Questions and Answers

(Opposite) skin will never be affected by make-up if it is diligently cleansed at the end of each day.

*1. Does make-up cause spots and blemishes by clogging the pores of the skin?*

No. Spots form because of certain hormonal activity which occurs at different times of life. In fact, make-up acts as a barrier against some damaging environmental conditions such as wind and dust.

*2. Why do lipsticks sometimes change colour after application.*

Invariably because of an acidic skin. This is usually indicated by naturally dark coloured lips. Use brown-tone lipsticks such as beiges, corals, apricots and peaches.

*3. Why do foundations sometimes change colour?*

Acidity again! Acidic skins tend to bring out the orange in foundations. Stick to beiges and light tans and use a mild astringent first as this neutralises the acid effect of the skin.

*4. Why does colour disappear so quickly from some faces?*

Because people with very oily skin absorb make-up to a greater degree than those with dry skin. Setting with loose powder will delay the process but some touching-up may be necessary.

**5. What can be done about disguising very dry skin?**

This is the most difficult of skin types to deal with when applying make-up. But you can take certain precautions to 'neutralise' the skin before foundation and powder are applied. Also, good moisturising beforehand and an oil-based foundation will help minimise the problem. Never use loose powder on dry skin.

**6. How can glossy lipstick be made to last longer?**

They really cannot, as they do come off all too easily. Use harder textured lipsticks, powder for extra staying powder, then apply a lip gloss.

**7. Are there any general guidelines on make-up for the older woman?**

Keep make-up light, and this means colour, texture and application, whether for a daytime or evening look.

Avoid cream foundations as they do age an older skin. Never use foundation around eyes as this accentuates wrinkles etc.

**8. How do you prevent lipstick 'bleeding' outside the lip line.**

Blot lipstick with a tissue and dust with loose powder before applying a second coat.

A beautifully made-up face is a subtle work of art — but don't stop there. Healthy, well-cut hair doubles the impact of your make-up efforts, and for ultra-sophistication, make full use of the lovely colours available in nail varnish for a truly co-ordinated effect.

This book has explained the basic techniques and professional ground rules from which all good make-up is created. Experience and the confidence that follows gives you the licence to experiment with this highly creative skill and to perhaps, one day, develop your own individual style.